MARTIN HONEYSETT

Micro Phobia

How to survive your computer and the technological revolution

BOOK CLUB ASSOCIATES
LONDON

First published 1982
This edition reprinted 1983 for
Book Club Associates
by arrangement with Century Publishing Co. Ltd.

ISBN 0 7126 0021 3 (paper)
ISBN 0 7126 0060 4 (cased)

Printed in Great Britain by
Richard Clay (The Chaucer Press) Ltd.,
Bungay, Suffolk

Some of the cartoons in this book were first seen in the magazines 'Corporate Video' and 'Personal Computer World.'

The development of the micro chip has been likened to the invention of the printing press, such is its importance to modern society. Video and computers are bound to have a great impact on our lives...

One of the first mass-produced products of micro technology was the calculator.

'I'm not playing with myself, I'm working my pocket calculator.'

'I've tried counting sheep
and I still can't get to sleep.'

Then came the games, bleeping their way into pubs and clubs. Games like computer tennis...

'We've had so many arguments we had to install an umpire.'

and Space Invaders...

'I hear the Space Invaders in this pub are really good.'

which are so popular…

'I don't mind you collecting beer mats but not Space Invaders.'

with almost everyone.

There are games which have invaded the home as well,

*'It'll pay for itself in the end.
He doesn't drink half the sherry he used to on his visits.'*

so that the whole family can play...

'We bought this game for Rex, really. He loves to chase the ball.'

all sorts of variations.

'Of course, the winner should really be spraying champagne about.'

'It's exhausted, I've been playing squash on it all afternoon.'

Adventurous people bought home computers…

'Take no notice, he's playing strip poker with his computer.'

'He's trying to get the computer to malfunction, so we can start the war.'

and tried their hand at advanced programming.

'I still think it's a bit of a risk, leaving it on the doorstep all day.'

It revolutionised their lives…

'The computer detects any movement outside and automatically moves the curtain.'

in simple ways...

'There are hundreds of sensors built into the bath surface, so that when you lose the soap it can tell you where it is.'

– in the garden,

'Yes dear, you can dig that one up.'

'Or if you prefer something a little more modern...'

'The trouble is, it's been programmed to cut a longer lawn.'

in cave...

'I used to meditate for hours over a question, now I can do it in seconds.'

or hovel.

'Harry likes to know exactly how poor we are.'

Micro computers have many uses at home.

'There must be a malfunction on the computer.'

They store information…

'It's all of those diet programmes you keep feeding into it.'

which can be retrieved…

*'Would you mind if I plugged in my computer?
I've made out my shopping list on it.'*

at any time.

'What excuse are you going to find this time?'

They are also aids to domesticity.

'It not only tells you your weight but also if your feet need washing.'

'We didn't realise he was dumb until we bought that thing.'

'You don't even talk to me any more'.

Of course, some don't find it easy.

'And I bought this one to explain the manual of the first one.'

And some just think they do.

'He thought he'd build his own microcomputer but unfortunately his eyesight's not all that good.'

In the home, video also has its uses.

'Dear video diary,
I got up this morning of June 8th, 1982...'

'He spends hours watching the birds feeding.'

'We don't get many visitors up here
but thanks to video we can see them lots of times.'

And for events such as marriages,

'Could you do it all again, Vicar,
I forgot to load the tape into the recorder.'

births...

'No, this morning's class is for those whose husband's won't be able to attend the birth.'

and deaths, video is indispensable.

'I'll get a minute or two of him waving goodbye before you close the lid.'

Holiday snaps need never be as boring again,

'This one shows us at Gatwick for three days during the air controllers' strike.'

'This is the one that started it all, our first visit to the topless beach at Corfu.'

and special occasions…

'They've yet to decide who'll get custody of the video.'

*'No, the video equipment's ours
but we had to hire the joint of beef.'*

and even not so special occasions...

'You know what they say, "A filmed kettle never boils".'

'Yes, that's better, a lot more dramatic.'

can be remembered in years to come.

*'Are you there Uncle Harry?
We're going to show the one of you falling under a bus.'*

Some, however, don't even need a home for their video pleasure and enjoyment.

'It's bad enough having him stand there all day watching, without him changing the channels as well.'

Of course, industry has not been slow to reap the benefits of the new technology.

'With this new computerised machinery we can have more of our men playing cards than ever before.'

From large businesses…

'The computer tells us when the brew has reached the required concentration.'

to small ones,

'We've used a computer to evaluate the structural strength of the project and I'm afraid the results aren't encouraging.'

*'Haven't you got one with less scruples?
It refuses to compute cash-in-hand estimates.'*

'We've fed all the permutations into the computer and it comes up with the same answer each time.'

and country,

'The computerised feeding system worked so well on the farm I had one installed in the house as well.'

'All right, you lot, which one of you programmed a dead rat onto Miss Pringle's computer?'

and offices everywhere,

the micro revolution has made its mark.

'I'm terribly sorry, Mrs Nisbitt, we've had no end of trouble since we installed a computer in the office.'

It is in areas such as office work that the impact of computers can be most easily appreciated.

'This is the one we use to send out final demands.'

In the office of the future, word processors and other computerised equipment…

'He likes to do all the letters himself now we've got a word processor.'

could replace up to 50 per cent of clerical staff,

'Thanks to microcomputers we've been able to get rid of four filing clerks and four filing cabinets.'

leaving the rest to the remaining members of staff...

who are highly trained to utilise the new technology.

'I'll arrange for some female company tonight. Fetch me my little black computer please, Mrs Biggs.'

Of course, expertise and equipment are important,

'I know they're cheaper but I still say we should have used a proper video company.'

with all types of organisations becoming users of both video and computer...

'We fed the ingredients of the new food into the computer and these are the brand names it's come up with.'

– abattoirs, for example.

'Phone the police, the computerised meat axe has gone beserk.'

And in education – in the primary school...

'We're hoping to get some more computers so we can teach them longer words.'

and secondary school,

'You will process a hundred times, Jenkins, "I must not play battleships on my computer during maths lessons"'.

in colleges and universities –

'It says it's the Student Union picket line and the strike committee are over at the Duke's Head.'

modern technology helps prepare today's students for tomorrow's new world.

'They may not be able to read and write but they certainly know how to push buttons by the time they leave here.'

Computers are used in the arts,

'Every now and then I let it do a self-portrait.'

for tuition,

'Computers have solved my problem of lack of instructors.'

in stores,

'It tells you the part number, whether it's in stock, and how many cuts and grazes you'll get trying to fit it.'

in the science laboratory,

'Of course it'll take us a while to learn how to use it properly.'

'What have you two been up to while I've been away?'

'I think it's found the formula, sir.'

in the doctor's surgery...

'I fed all your symptoms into the computer, Mr Bilkins, and it died.'

or even at the fire station.

'We feed the address into the computer and it shows us a map of the area together with the exact location of the fire.'

And robots…

'I'm all for computers, they do all the dull, boring jobs for you.'

will start doing the routine work.

'Thanks to computers we don't have to manhandle radioactive waste at all now.'

Video, too, has many roles in the working world.

'Oh dear, they've had one of those morale boosting videos at the factory again.'

It can put out the management message,

'We thought it would be a lot safer if we made a video report to the shareholders, rather than a live one.'

be used as training aids...

'I sometimes wonder if we're not over-indulging the staff with these video films, Henderson.'

and as sales aids.

'There's a video cassette to see you, Mr Brown'.

'I don't quite see how this will sell machine tools but what the hell, he's paying for it.'

'Actually we were wondering if you could make the videos a little less interesting.'

The world of medicine...

'Play that bit back again nurse,
I don't think I got it quite right.'

is equally important,

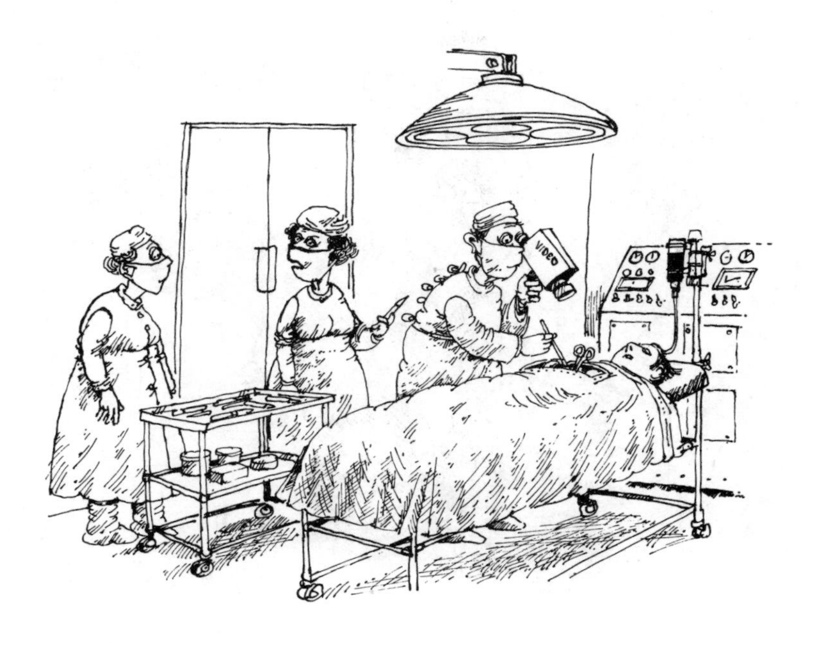

'The cameraman fainted but fortunately Dr Wimbold knows how to fix it.'

as is the arts.

'He hasn't really made it as a director, nobody's pirated any of his films.'

'I've got three of them in different parts of the station.'

'Do you want the one or two hour cassette?'

Then there's traffic surveillance,

'I think there's a pigeon sitting on top of the London Road camera again.'

the lone entrepreneur...

'I used to shout myself hoarse sometimes, before I got this.'

and travel companies.

'I'm afraid the video of your hotel isn't finished yet, we'll have to transfer you to another cassette.'

And apart from being an aid to industry,

'He was late for the launching,
fortunately we recorded the whole thing on video.'

there's always the hairdresser,

'We film the back of the head so you can see it in the comfort of your own home.'

'They're very difficult to mate in captivity, we thought a few erotic films might help.'

and those important events that need to be recorded for posterity...

'Hang on, Groates, if you're walking off to die I want to get it on tape.'

– not to mention the less important.

'After another week he should be ready to record his first jump.'

Video also has its place in crime prevention,

'Unfortunately it was after the robbery that we discovered the camera was wrongly positioned.'

'I'm afraid we're unable to show you the programme at the moment because the video recorder's been stolen.'

not to mention crime itself.

'They've arrested him for the computer fraud and the computer as an accessory.'

Video and computers both have their applications.

'Fred's very advanced, he uses a computer on all our robberies now.'

Teletex is another development of the new technology. Using a modified TV set,

'He's just made another five million profit. Now he wants to find out who sells the cheapest champagne.'

many types of information can be received.

'It's run by the local WI.
It's a gossip data service.'

It's been suggested it might replace conventional...

'It may be more up to date than a newspaper but it's not so good for lighting the fire.'

news media,

'They're always the same, these places, nothing but old copies of 'Punch' to look at.'

while in conjunction with cable television you will be able to shop,

'Yes, they look fine to me dear.'

use your bank,

'No dear, for loans over a thousand it says you have to get down on two knees.'

'It's a special egg-throwing button.'

or take part in consumer research surveys...

– all from the comfort of your own home.

'He doesn't even have to walk to the job centre any more.'

Even the humble telephone seems different somehow.

'Now, thanks to this, I don't miss any obscene calls when I'm out.'

To help people use and understand computers there are community computer centres. Such facilities are important,

'I'm afraid you've made a mistake ladies, the bingo hall is next door.'

for in years to come the new technology is bound to play an increasingly prominent role in our lives.

'It's nature's way of adapting, son.
Now that computers do all our brainwork we don't need such big heads.'